The Boy and the Stars

To Frank Kappler
with grateful good wishes

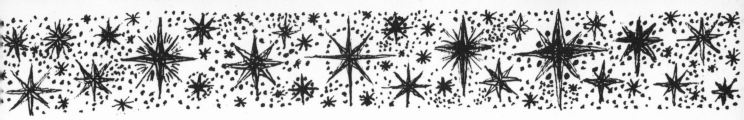

THE BOY AND THE STARS

A Lyrical Tale of Dante Alighieri; The Boy

Written by Francesca Gulì Illustrated by Patricia Walsh

The Golden Quill Press Publishers Francestown, New Hampshire

Library of Congress Catalog Card Number 65-23536

Printed in the United States of America

Dedicated to

SISTER MARGARET TERESA
whose classroom was not a classroom
but a place where stars walked
and stars talked.

INTRODUCTION

To my knowledge a story of Dante *as a little boy,* lyrical or otherwise, has never been written. Although THE BOY AND THE STARS was written with children in mind, the author nourishes the hope that its audience will be well-peopled by members of the elder sector of children over twenty-one! The sources used, besides the great poet's own works, include writings from the famous essay on Dante by Boccaccio to Father Gerard Walsh's brilliant collection of lectures.

Where I have used imagination in the poem I have done so liberally but never at the expense of an historical fact, a statement I would bear out by calling kind attention to the Notes at the end of the book. I have, however, chosen to agree with the competent authorities who state that Dante's mother died before he reached the age of reason or when he was about six or seven years old. And Dante is about six when the poem ends.

The motivating force behind the writing of this poem is to generate interest in the person Dante beyond the confines of the scholarly, because indeed he himself was a man most humanely human, who loved mankind and whose very purpose in writing his masterpiece, THE DIVINE COMEDY, was, to quote the poet's own words, "to lift those living in this life from a state of misery and to guide them to a state of happiness."

Thus I have tried here to portray the Lone Eagle of Italian letters only as the lovable fledgling of great promise he assuredly must have been, and would wish the poem to be judged on that premise alone.

I am indebted to my good friend, Patricia Walsh, for her beautiful art accompanying and embellishing the poem and to Sister Margaret Teresa, Dante scholar and Professor of English at Nazareth College, without whose initial inspiration this poem might never have been written.

FRANCESCA GULÌ

Rochester, New York
July 1964

Let only the heart heed; let the heart listen well
To this story of the child of heaven and hell . . .

In the year twelve hundred and sixty-five

When birds in the trees and bees in the hive

Flew heavy and full on warm golden wings,
In an emerald country of peasants and kings

Of mountain and meadow and blue placid seas
Of village and valley, of towers and trees

In a city whose name meant flowers and bloom
In a yellow stone house, in a little stone room

Came into the world, was born to this earth
A baby no bigger than babies at birth.

He was lusty and new and red as a rose
With a fine broad forehead and a rather large nose.

"His eyes will be light," thought his mother aloud.
"We'll name him for Grandfather; he will be proud."

But *Durante* seemed old

and pompous, she thought.

"We'll call him Dante, then,

for short."

And for many a grey dawn, for many a bright noon
She could be heard singing to her little son.

Alone in her chamber, holding him near,
Now in her happiness, now in her fear

She would wait for his smile,

comfort his cry

Singing the while her lullaby:

18

"He shall eat of the fruit of the laurel tree,
And drink of the waters of the spring.
Clothed as a shepherd he shall walk as a king,
And the voice of the ages round him ring;
The ages round him ring."

Lady Bella's Lullaby

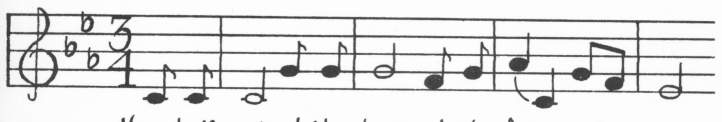

He shall eat of the fruit of the lau- rel tree

and drink of the wa-ters of the spring. Clothed as a shep-herd

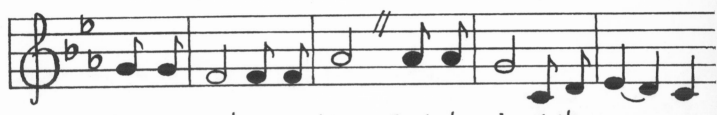

he shall walk as a king And the voice of the a — ges

round him ring. The a — ges round him ring.

rallentando

And the infant days passed as the days of the rose
In her spring's first sleep, in her winter's repose.

And it wasn't long till Dante could walk in the sun
And speak words he wondered and delighted on.

Already he knew the "Ave" by heart —
The prayer of morning he repeated at night

His mother had taught-- and a psalm or two
They would half-sing together as he loved to do.

And sweet was her voice and her face was fair
And blue her eyes and golden her hair,

Long golden hair that she twisted and spun
Into braids round her head where it sat like a crown.

And happy were the hours that he spent at her knee
When she spoke of God and eternity.

And his wonder grew wide and his yearning deep
And he'd ply her with questions till it was time to sleep:

"Why is the swallow
Able to fly,
And does he reach
Heaven, bye and bye?

Where do the stars go
In the bright day's light,
And why do we see them
Only at night?"

And Lady Bella would smile and gather him close
And kiss him and say, looking long in his face,

"Too great a wonder for such a wee head . . .
Come. Let's fetch Andrea; it's time for bed."

And Andrea would come to Lady Bella's aid.
She was big and robust, more than friend and maid,

And lifting her charge high up in her arm
She would bear him away to his little room.

And often he asked, "Is my mother not well?"
And she answered, "She is frail, little one, and pale,

As pale as the Rose of the Silver Moon
That blooms a June morning and sheds before noon.

Pale she is and beautiful, a queen in her way.
But I fear," she whispered, "she'll not last a long day."

And on those days when Lady Bella lay confined to her bed
Little Dante sought out his father instead.

Together they would take long walks when they could -
If he had been good (and he was most often good,

Save when he was naughty or spoke out of turn,
For then he was ashamed and his cheeks would burn.)

How he loved to walk past the crowded square
Among the sounds and sights to be seen everywhere!

Where Old Man Pietro sat mending his guitar
And a little lame juggler threw balls in the air,

Past the church of Saint Martin and Beautiful Saint John,
Past the high city gates and stone walls and on -

Where the air smelled sweet and birds flew and wheeled,
Where the voices of the vineyards and the whispers of the field

Stirred a clamor in his heart till he wanted to shout
And lie on the grass and dance all about,

For these solitary byways he loved the very best
And here they would linger till the sun fell in the west.

And on the brighest days, when he was two years and three
They walked to the bridge of Holy Trinity.

There along the river he would nearly hold his breath
To see the tiny shops that hung in clusters underneath

And he'd buy a pomegranate for a penny, or a pear
Or a length of scarlet ribbon for his mother's hair;

And he'd ride on father's shoulder till he seemed to touch
The spires and the towers that he loved so much!

Then there were Sundays when they went to church and prayed
And he'd wear his best tunic and a belt of gold braid.

And often on that day about a quarter past four
Old friends would knock on the family door.

There was his teacher, Ser Romano, who taught the alphabet
And the Manuals and Psalms he already knew in part.

And Messer Donati, the kindly man next door,
And one whom Dante thought quite special for

Ser Brun was a learned man and spoke in Latin.
He wore shoes of finest leather lined with satin

With a great green jewel sewn over each toe
That walked when he walked with a great green glow.

Some called him master and some called him sage
For he was passing wise and of venerable age.

How Dante loved to listen to the stories he would tell! -
Of earth and of creation, of heaven and hell;

But of all the tales of Planets, of Jupiter and Mars,
He loved best of all the stories of the Stars.

For then Ser Bruns' eyes gleamed like the jewels on his toe
And his old voice crackled for *he* seemed to know

The secrets of the universe and the mystery of earth
And, according to the stars, just what a man was worth!

"The sun was in Gemini, my boy, when you were born.
And high in her heaven bright Vega shone,

Great blue-white Vega of the Golden Lyre,
Bright, brilliant Vega of the blue-white fire!"

And he smiled when he said it and he looked very wise
And Dante was silent, and looking long in his eyes

Said, "If stars decree us wise, can the stars make us good?"
And Ser Brun smiled and patted his head.

"Only follow your star, son. Follow your star!"
And he marvelled in his beard, "This boy will go far."

And the days passed for Dante in the sun and rain
And he soon learned to read and to write with a pen.

His mother, Lady Bella, seemed almost well again
And he would do his letters and read to her and then

One early April evening he thought he had
Never seen her more beautiful - and never so sad.

And she murmured as he bent to kiss her goodnight,
"Look to the light, my child," and pressed his hand tight.

He thought Andrea wept as she held up the lamp
For long after prayers her face was damp.

And he thought of his mother as he lay in his bed,
Thought of her sadness and the words she had said...

He loved all light: The light of morning pale as pearl
And light of afternoon with the sun turned on full.

And even light at nighttime when there was no light at all
Save his own long shadow kneelng up a wall.

This night, he thought, he would not go to sleep;
He would stay wide awake; a watch he would keep.

And when Andrea and her lamp
   disappeared out of sight
He stole to the window and
   pushed it out to the night.

And there where the spires slept
   with bells in their throat
And skylight and window
   spurned drawbridge and moat

The boy paused as one pauses
   to quench a great thirst.
For there, for the first time,
   for the very first

In the black arc of night,
   in the vast nocturnal hours
Dante found the wondrous
   world of the stars!

There beyond the casement, past the wrought-iron bars
Hung the brilliant and the white and the trembling stars.

In bunches here, now there, now on a long silver ribbon
Scattered near, scattered far, over all the whole heaven!

Held fast, held suspended, sparkling and clear
Like the many-splendored lights of a giant chandelier!

Why had they not told him, not told him before
How very beautiful they were

How great it all was, how awesome to see
And so struck with the wonder and the beauty was he

The walls of his room fell away at the sight
And he stood alone in the ebony night.

And his heart beat loud

and his breath came still

As though something of power,

something of will

Moved him beyond the small space of his breast
And he wanted to fly as a bird from its nest!

And he stood a long time, caught in their spell
Till he was almost afraid, till he almost fell.

But the stars held him fast as they whirled round his head
And he walked where they walked in their silvery tread.

High over rooftops, up over towers
Alone through the night, at one with his stars.

And he thought of his mother and her sweet sad face.
Oh could she but know of the dream that was his!

And the lovely lady of the face so fair
Seemed to hold out her hand; he walked with her there -

And suddenly he grew tired and he stood quite still
And kneeling very slowly sank down to the sill

As though he would not yet take leave of his prize.
For much had been the wonder that filled his young eyes.

And he slept where he lay in the light of those stars
Until Andrea found him in the small morning hours.

How long he had lain there she could not tell.
Only his face was warm and he seemed to smile,

Though he never woke as she tucked him in bed
And lay down beside him and pillowed his head.

For how could she know as she nestled him close
Of the very beautiful dream that was his,

How in the black arc of night, in the vast nocturnal hours
He had found the wondrous world of the stars,

How the walls of his room fell away at the sight
And he stood alone in the ebony night.

NOTES

page 9.   . . . *the child of heaven and hell*

When he grew to manhood Dante wrote THE DIVINE COMEDY, a long epic poem in three parts or canticles: Inferno, Purgatorio, and Paradiso, describing an imaginary journey through hell, purgatory and heaven.

page 11.   *In the year twelve hundred and sixty-five*

Dante was born in the 13th century, nearly seven hundred years ago, during that period known as The Middle Ages, that is, the 1000 years between the fall of Rome in the 5th century and the beginning of the Renaissance in the 15th.

page 12.   *In an emerald country of peasants and kings*

The country is Italy during the reign of Manfred, son of Emperor Frederick II, who was defeated by Charles of Anjou, King of Naples and Sicily.

page 13.   *In a city whose name meant flowers and bloom*

The city is Florence, located on the banks of the Arno River, 145 miles northwest of Rome in the province of the Tuscany. *Florence* means "flowery" or "flourishing," hence bloom or prosperity.

page 15.   *Durante seemed old and pompous* . . .

Durante was Dante's grandfather on his mother's side. The name means "enduring" or "everlasting." *Dante* means "giving."

page 18. *Singing the while her lullaby*

The words of Lady Bella's lullaby are adapted from the dream that Dante's mother had of him a few months before he was born as recorded by Boccaccio, Dante's first real biographer. All the signs seemed to foretell his future greatness as a poet: *the laurel tree* . . . In those days a poet was crowned with a wreath of laurel. *the waters of the spring* . . . This refers to the spring from which according to Greek legend gushed waters of inspiration sought by those devoted to the arts. *Clothed as a shepherd* . . . Because of political troubles Dante was forced to leave Italy when still a young man and remained in exile the rest of his life. The music for the lullaby is the original composition of the author.

page 23. *Already he knew "Ave" by heart*

Dante said the prayer, the "Ave Maria," morning and night every day of his life.

page 23. *. . . and a psalm or two*

Committing the Psalms and parts of the Bible to memory was part of the pre-school training of those days.

page 24. *And sweet was her voice and her face was fair*

Donna Gabriella degli Abati, or Lady Bella as we know her, was obviously a woman of some breeding. It is not beyond possibility therefore to suppose that she herself loved poetry and song, and indeed was thus the better able to engender the very dream of her only child's future glory!

page 27. *And Andrea would come to Lady Bella's aid*

In the *only* fictitious character of Andrea we see any one of the kindly neighboring women who must have helped Lady Bella in her need. For her to have died so young, it can safely be assumed she remained in frail health after the birth of her son until her death six or seven years later.

page 28. *Little Dante sought out his father instead*

Dante's father, Alaghiero di Bellincione di Alaghiero (the name was later simplified to Alighieri) was a plain and simple man, a notary or small banker of those times. He died when Dante was twelve years old, leaving him orphaned then of both father and mother.

page 30. *How he loved to walk past the crowded square*

The squares of the town or "piazze" are still popular in Italy today. Dante's house was located in the Piazza San Martino in that part of the city called Porta San Piero, "Gate of Saint Peter."

page 32. *Past the church of Saint Martin and*
Beautiful Saint John

The church of Saint Martin is in the Piazza San Martino directly across the street from the site of Dante's home. He was christened, however, at the Baptistry of the larger and more beautiful church of San Giovanni in Florence.

page 34. *They walked to the bridge of Holy Trinity*

Ponte Santa Trinita', this famous old bridge of Florence, was constructed in 1252, just thirteen years before Dante was born and was noted for its graceful arches.

page 36.   *Ser Brun was a learned man . . .*

A Florentine politician, an amateur astrologist, and one of Dante's later teachers, Brunetto Latini predicted the boy's future greatness. He was fifty-five years old when Dante was born and died at the venerable age of eighty-four when Dante was only twenty-nine.

page 40.   *The sun was in Gemini . . .*

This is the horoscope of Dante's birthday which most authorities fix as occurring in the later part of May — May 27 — 1265. The great star Vega is in the constellation of Lyra, or The Lyre, once fancied to be the magic musical instrument of the mythical poet, Orpheus, and hence symbol of culture or the arts.

page 46.   *Dante found the wondrous world of the stars*

Dante's place among the world's great poetic geniuses gives credibility to the ensuing vision or dream and to the intellectual precocity of the lad. Indeed the stars fascinated Dante all his life and it is interesting to note that each of the three canticles of THE DIVINE COMEDY ends with the word "stelle" or stars, symbolic of the constant aspiration of poem and poet toward the highest things.